ROCK & POP

VOCA

ROCK & POP

TRINITY
COLLEGE LONDON

THE EXAM AT A GLANCE

For your Rock & Pop exam you will need to perform a set of **three songs** and one of the **Session skills** assessments, either **Playback** or **Improvising**. You can choose the order in which you perform your set-list.

Song 1

Choose a song from this book

OR from www.trinityrock.com/downloads.

Song 2

Choose a different song from this book

OR from www.trinityrock.com/downloads

OR perform a song you have chosen yourself: this could be your own cover version or a song you have written. It should be at the same level as the songs in this book.

Song 3: Technical focus

Choose one of the Technical focus songs from this book, which cover three specific technical elements.

Session skills

Choose either **Playback** or **Improvising**.

When you are preparing for your exam please check on **www.trinityrock.com** for the most up-to-date information and requirements as these can change from time to time.

CONTENTS

Trinity College London's Rock & Pop syllabus and supporting publications have been devised and produced in association with Faber Music and Peters Edition London.

Trinity College London
Registered office:
89 Albert Embankment
London SE1 7TP UK
T + 44 (0)20 7820 6100
F + 44 (0)20 7820 6161
E music@trinitycollege.co.uk
www.trinitycollege.co.uk

Registered in the UK. Company no. 02683033
Charity no. 1014792
Patron HRH The Duke of Kent KG

Copyright © 2012 Trinity College London
First published in 2012 by Trinity College London

Cover and book design by Chloë Alexander
Brand development by Andy Ashburner @ Caffeinehit (www.caffeinehit.com)
Photographs courtesy of Rex Features Limited.
Printed in England by Caligraving Ltd

Audio produced, mixed and mastered by Tom Fleming
Vocal arrangements by Oliver Weeks
Backing tracks arranged by Tom Fleming
Vocal Consultant: Heidi Pegler
Musicians
Vocals: Bo Walton, Brendan Reilly & Alison Symons
Keyboards: Oliver Weeks
Guitar & Bass: Tom Fleming
Bass: Ben Hillyard
Drums: George Double
Studio Engineer: Joel Davies www.thelimehouse.com

All rights reserved

ISBN: 978-0-85736-256-8

SONGS GREASE

Frankie Valli
Words and Music by Barry Gibb

SONGS

BOTH SIDES NOW

Joni Mitchell
Words and Music by Joni Mitchell

♩ = 92 **Gently**

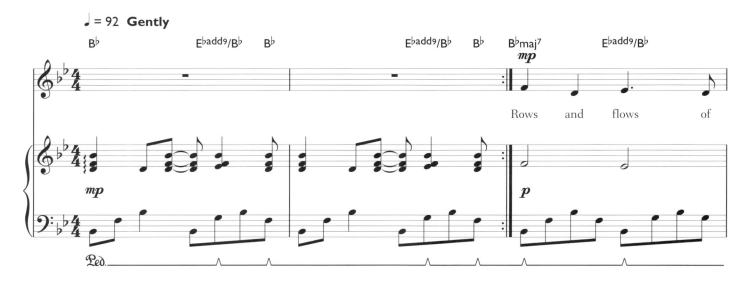

Rows and flows of

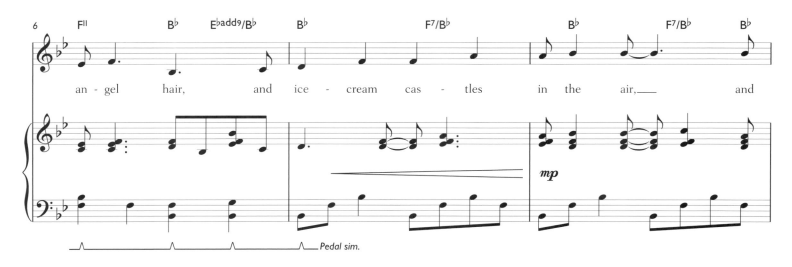

an - gel hair, and ice - cream cas - tles in the air,___ and

fea - ther can - yons ev - 'ry - where,___ I've looked at clouds that

Alternative lower key available from www.trinityrock.com

SONGS NO SOUND BUT THE WIND

Editors

Words and Music by Thomas Smith, Christopher Urbanowicz, Russell Leetch and Edward Lay

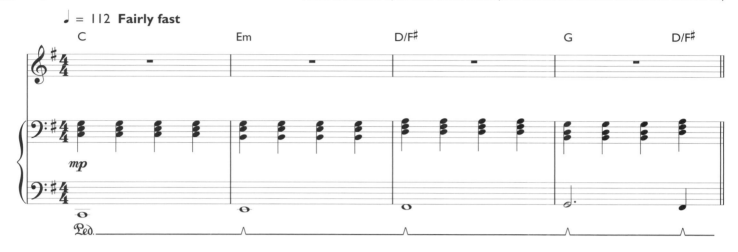

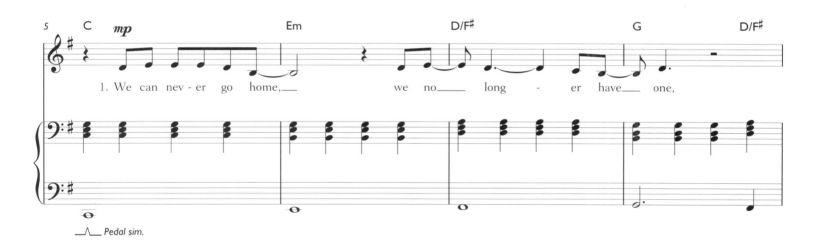

1. We can nev-er go home, we no long - er have one,

I'll help you car-ry the load, I'll car-ry you in my arms.

Alternative higher key available from www.trinityrock.com

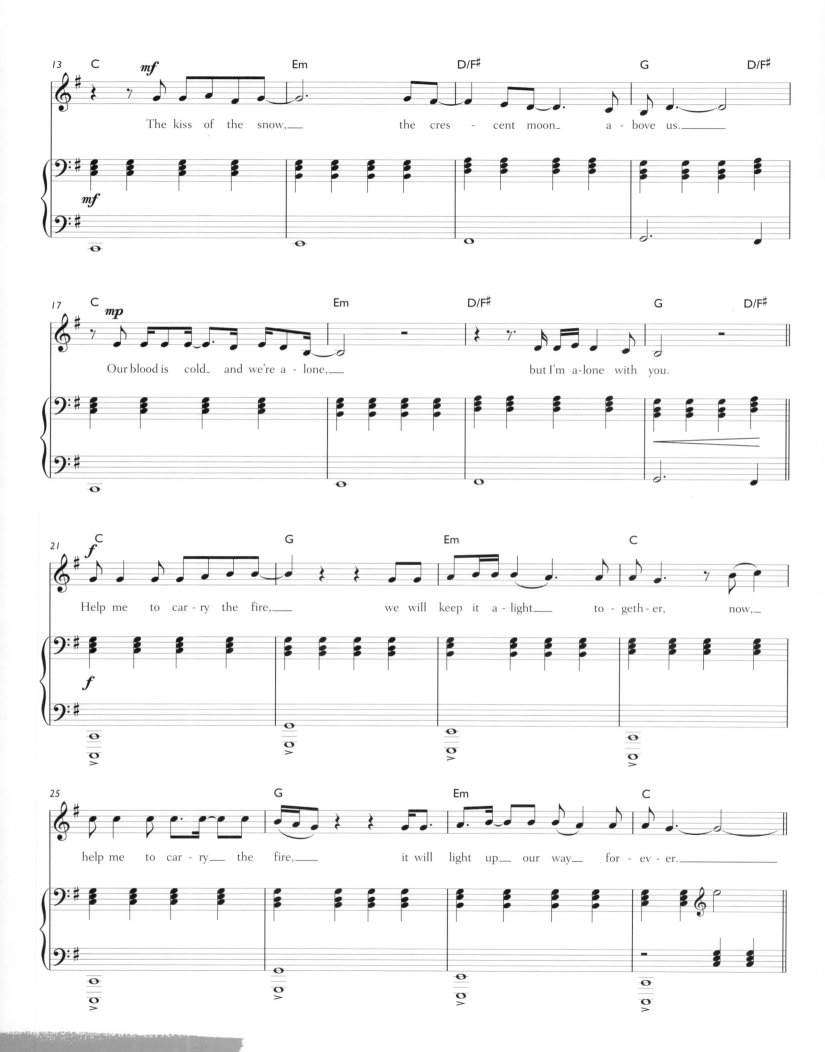

Help me to car-ry the fire,___ we will keep it a-light to-geth-er,

help me to car-ry___ the fire,___ it will light our way___ for-ev-er.

SONGS MEAN JUMPER BLUES

Blind Lemon Jefferson
Words and Music by Blind Lemon Jefferson

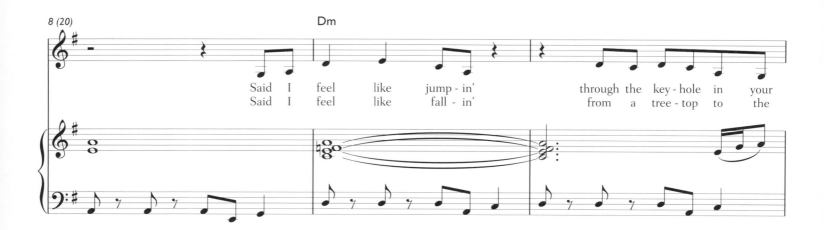

KILLING ME SOFTLY WITH HIS SONG

In your exam, you will be assessed on the following elements:

1 Breathing

Work out where to breathe – make sure you don't breathe mid-phrase.
'Killing Me Softly' has two, two-bar phrases followed by a longer four-bar phrase. Breathe after each of the two-bar phrases, then take a big breath and sing through the four-bar phrase, so that it holds together. Try to avoid becoming tense when you take big breaths.

Try singing bars 15–18 in one breath, so that you keep a forward momentum in bar 16.

2 Counting

'Killing Me Softly' opens with four bars' rest for the vocalist. The vocals do not start on the first beat of bar 5: the first entry comes in just after the second beat. Count four full bars, then '1 and 2 and'. This will help you come in at the right place.

The next entry (bar 9) also comes in just after the second beat, but entries later in the song are slightly different. Watch out for:
- bar 13: where the vocals enter on the second beat
- bar 30: where the vocals enter just after the third beat.

3 Long notes

Make sure that you hold the long notes at the ends of phrases for their full length. Use plenty of support to help keep the long notes in tune.

TRACK 9 — demo
TRACK 10 — backing

KILLING ME SOFTLY WITH HIS SONG

Roberta Flack

Words by Norman Gimbel • Music by Charles Fox

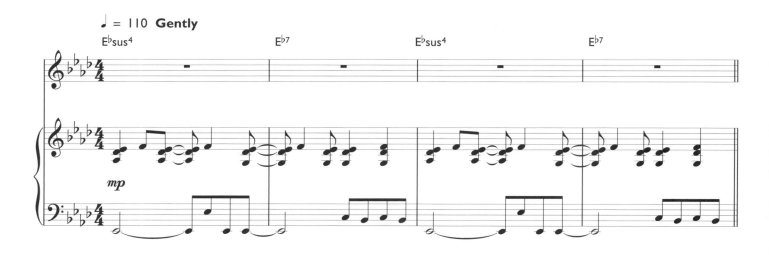

I heard he sang___ a good song, I___ heard he

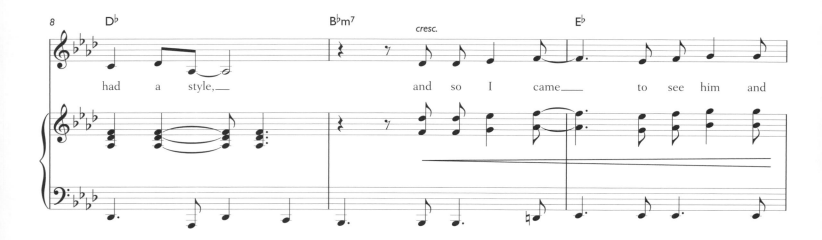

had a style,___ and so I came___ to see him and

Alternative higher key available from www.trinityrock.com

YOUR PAGE NOTES

I NEED A DOLLAR

In your exam, you will be assessed on the following technical elements:

1 Breathing

Work out where to breathe – make sure you don't breathe mid-phrase. 'I Need A Dollar' has two, two-bar phrases followed by a longer four-bar phrase. Breathe after each of the two bar phrases, then take a big breath and sing through the four-bar phrase, so that it holds together. Try to avoid becoming tense when you take big breaths.

2 Rhythm

The rhythm of 'I Need A Dollar' may look complicated on the page but the vocal line tends to follow the rhythm of the words. Try to feel the flow of the words and make the rhythms sound natural. There is a steady ♪ beat in the accompaniment throughout most of the song – this should help keep you in time.

The same rhythm repeats for much of the song. But it changes slightly on the last page – be ready for this.

3 Pitching the intervals

An interval is the distance in pitch between any two notes. Most of the intervals in 'I Need A Dollar' are quite small: these are relatively easy to pitch.

Some phrases start with larger intervals. Bar 5 opens with a fifth and bar 9 opens with an octave. Make sure that these intervals are accurate and sound confident.

I NEED A DOLLAR

Aloe Blacc

Words and Music by Jeffrey Silverman, Leon Michels, Nicholas Movshon and Aloe Blacc

Alternative higher key available from www.trinityrock.com

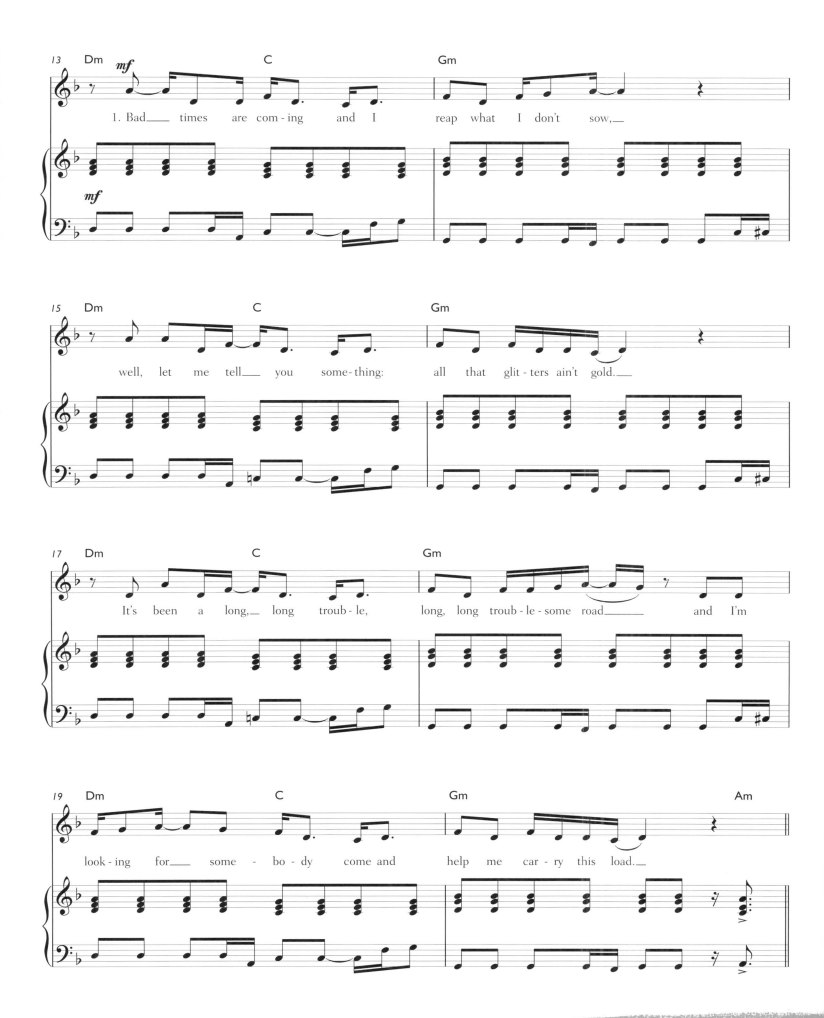

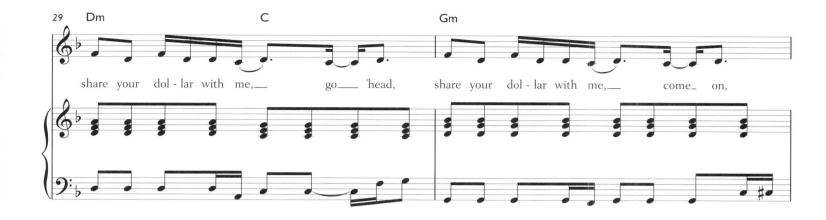

share your dol-lar with me,___ go___'head, share your dol-lar with me,___ come_ on,

share your dol-lar, give me your dol-lar, share your dol-lar with me,___ come_ on,

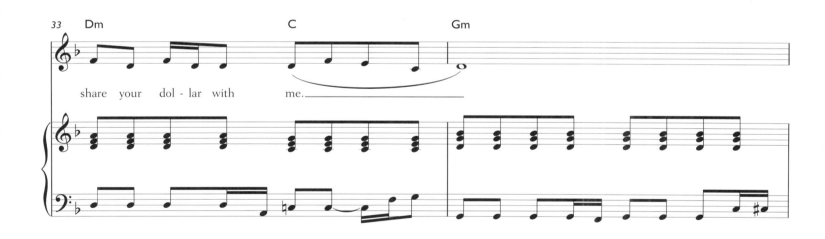

share your dol-lar with me.___

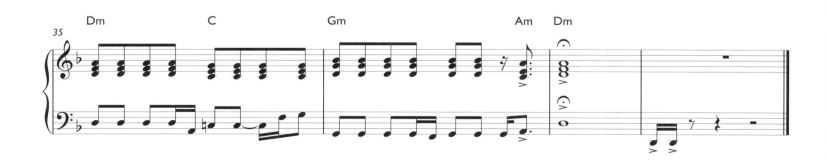

GREASE

Frankie Valli

'Grease' is the theme song from the 1978 film *Grease* starring John Travolta and Olivia Newton-John. The film is based on the 1971 musical of the same name which centres on the lives and loves of students in a 1950s high school.

Although the film is set in the 1950s, the song 'Grease' has more in common with 1970s disco music, with its danceable four-to-the-floor beat. The song was written by Barry Gibb of the Bee Gees. It was sung on *Grease: The Original Soundtrack from the Motion Picture* by Frankie Valli, an American singer who had a successful solo career and was also the frontman of the popular 1960s band the Four Seasons.

PERFORMANCE HINTS & TIPS

'Grease' is a lively, exuberant song with a strong disco beat. The whole song needs to be sung rhythmically, led by the natural flow of the words.

The rests are crucial in order for the song to sit in the right groove. Be careful not to sing through these rests.

Make sure you come off promptly at the end of bar 28, as the backing takes over.

Bars 34–37 build up towards the climax at bar 37, which is marked $\boldsymbol{f\!f}$. This stands for *fortissimo*, which means very loud. The final note of this phrase needs to be held very strongly and securely.

Remember that if this key doesn't suit your voice there is an alternative version available from www.trinityrock.com in a higher key.

'We *got* a *lovin'* thing, *we* gotta *feed* it *right*'

BOTH SIDES NOW

Joni Mitchell

Singer-songwriters flourished during the 1970s, particularly on the folk-rock scene, and Joni Mitchell was one of the most successful of these. Her songs relate personal experiences; they are often conversational and descriptive, with bittersweet observations. Her voice is pure and wide-ranging and she often accompanies herself on guitar or piano.

'Both Sides Now' first appeared on the album *Clouds*, released in 1969. There have been many covers of this song, including versions by Judy Collins, Davy Graham and Tori Amos.

'Both Sides Now' is a contemplative song. The clouds represent the singer's life. She has looked at them from all perspectives, but still does not understand them – the same applies to her life. You should try to portray this reflective mood. Try singing the song in two ways: as though you were telling someone else a story, then as though you were singing it to yourself.

Backing vocals have been included on the backing track of this song. Be sure to concentrate on your own line and don't let this put you off.

There is some interesting dynamic contrast and shading in this song. The vocals start moderately quietly (*mp*) and stay at this level until bar 16, where it changes to *mf* (moderately loud) for one bar and then immediately drops down to *mp* again in the next bar. Make sure you can hear the difference in this bar.

Hold the long notes in bars 28-29 and 30-31 for their full length: use plenty of support. In bar 28, get gradually quieter where the *diminuendo* is marked.

Remember that if this key doesn't suit your voice there is an alternative version available from www.trinityrock.com in a lower key.

'It's cloud *illusions I recall'*

NO SOUND BUT THE WIND

Editors

Editors are a British indie rock band with a dark, often melancholic sound. The four members met while studying music technology at Stafford University.

'No Sound But The Wind' was first released as a single in Belgium in 2010. Since then, the song has gone through many changes. It also features on *The Twilight Saga: New Moon* soundtrack.

PERFORMANCE HINTS & TIPS

The rhythm in bar 17 of this song might look rather complicated, but focus on the natural rhythm of the words and it should feel quite easy.

If you find it difficult to sing 'it will light up our way forever' – including the long note in bars 28–29 – in one breath, take a breath just before the word 'forever'.

The quiet ending (bar 37 onwards) needs a lot of control. It is marked 'freely', so the rhythm need not be precise, but make sure that the first beat of the bar is always exactly in time with the backing track.

Remember that if this key doesn't suit your voice there is an alternative version available from www.trinityrock.com in a higher key.

'Help *me* to *carry* the *fire*'

MEAN JUMPER BLUES

Blind Lemon Jefferson

'Mean Jumper Blues' is a 12-bar blues first recorded by the Texan blues singer and guitarist Blind Lemon Jefferson. Like most blues (early American black music originally performed by one singer accompanied on guitar or banjo), 'Mean Jumper Blues' has four beats in a bar and is built around a three-line verse, where the second line is a repeat of the first.

As a young man, Blind Lemon Jefferson was a poverty-stricken wandering street musician. Despite this, he built up a good reputation and, in 1925, became one of the first country blues musicians to get a recording contract. These early recordings went on to have a big influence on rock musicians. Many artists have covered his songs, including Bob Dylan, Grateful Dead and Counting Crows. Blind Lemon Jefferson froze to death in 1929 during a snow storm, having had a heart attack.

'Mean Jumper Blues' does not start on the first beat of the bar but on the final ♪; this is usually known as a 'pick up' (it is also sometimes called an upbeat or *anacrusis*). Be sure to come in at the right place: you will need to count.

The song starts *mf* (*mezzo forte* = moderately loud) and stays that way for most of the song, but it is marked *f* (*forte* = loud) at bar 28. Make sure there is a clear difference between *mf* and *f*. Remember to drop right down to *mp* (*mezzo piano* = moderately quiet) at bar 36.

'*If you* jump *this* time, *baby*, you *won't* jump *no* more'

KILLING ME SOFTLY WITH HIS SONG

Roberta Flack

Roberta Flack comes from North Carolina, USA. She grew up in a musical family and received a scholarship to study music at university aged only 15. She began her career as a music teacher, eventually being discovered singing at a jazz club, accompanying herself on piano. She was then signed to the Atlantic record label.

Roberta Flack's singing style is cool and sophisticated and she is most well-known for her slow, jazz-infused ballads. 'Killing Me Softly With His Song' was released in 1973 and became her second No. 1 hit. The song has been covered many times, most famously by the hip-hop band the Fugees.

PERFORMANCE · HINTS & TIPS ·

'Killing Me Softly' is a sophisticated ballad where the phrasing and breathing are very important. The music ebbs and flows gently and so do the dynamics – there is a feeling of rise and fall throughout the song, but it is never really loud.

Be ready for the accidentals (E♮) in bars 15 and 16.

Remember that if this key doesn't suit your voice there is an alternative version available from www.trinityrock.com in a higher key.

'Singing my life with his words'

I NEED A DOLLAR

Aloe Blacc

Los Angeles singer-songwriter Aloe Blacc's single 'I Need A Dollar' is from his album *Good Things*. The lyrics of this song tell of someone who has been made jobless by the recession. It soon became a credit-crunch anthem, popular on television shows and in commercials, leading to it becoming a hit single in 2010.

Aloe Blacc has worked both as a consultant accountant (under his real name Egbert Nathaniel Dawkins) and as an MC. The song has an interesting mix of influences, with elements of soul, jazz, pop and rap.

· PERFORMANCE · HINTS & TIPS ·

'I Need A Dollar' is quite a wordy song – try speaking the words through several times before you learn to sing it. Articulate the consonants clearly – they will give the song energy and enable the listener to understand you more easily.

In bar 9 there is an octave leap on the second beat, which you may find tricky at first. Listen to the demo on the CD a lot, it will help you pitch the note.

Remember that if this key doesn't suit your voice there is an alternative version available from www.trinityrock.com in a higher key.

'Bad *times* are *coming* and I, reap *what* I *don't* sow'

PLAYBACK

For your exam, you can choose either Playback or Improvising (see page 35). If you choose Playback, you will be asked to perform some music you have not seen or heard before.

In the exam, you will be given the song chart and the examiner will play a recording of the music on CD. You will hear several two-bar phrases on the CD: you should sing each of them straight back in turn. There's a rhythm track going throughout, which helps you keep in time. There should not be any gaps in the music.

In the exam you will have two chances to perform with the CD:
- First time – for practice
- Second time – for assessment.

You should listen to the audio, copying what you hear; you can also read the music from the song chart. Here are some practice song charts which are also on the CD in this book. The music is printed without text and may be sung to any vowel (with or without consonant) or to sol-fa.

Practice playback 1

TRACK 13

Practice playback 2

TRACK 14

SESSION SKILLS

IMPROVISING

For your exam, you can choose either Playback (see page 34), or Improvising. If you choose to improvise, you will be asked to improvise over a backing track that you haven't heard before in a specified style.

In the exam, you will be given a song chart and the examiner will play a recording of the backing track on CD. The backing track consists of a passage of music played on a loop. You should improvise a melody line over the backing track.

In the exam you will have two chances to perform with the CD:
- First time – for practice
- Second time – for assessment.

Here are some practice improvisation charts which are also on the CD in this book. The music is printed without text and may be sung to any vowel (with or without consonant) or to sol-fa.

Practice improvisation 1

♩ = 60 **Ballad**

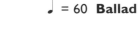

Practice improvisation 2

♩ = 88 **Rock**

CHOOSING A SONG FOR YOUR EXAM

There are lots of options to help you choose your three songs for the exam. For Songs 1 and 2, you can choose a song which is:

* from this book
* from www.trinityrock.com/downloads

Or for Song 2 you can choose a song which is:

* sheet music from a printed or online source
* your own arrangement of a song or a song you have written yourself (see page 37).

You can perform the song unaccompanied or with a backing track (minus the solo instrument/voice). If you like, you can create a backing track yourself (or with friends).

For Grade 2, the song should last between one and three-and-a-half minutes, and the level of difficulty should be similar to your other songs. When choosing a song, think about:

* Does it work for my instrument/voice?
* Are there any technical elements that are too difficult for me? (If so, perhaps save it for when you do the next grade.)
* Do I enjoy singing it?
* Does it work with my other songs to create a good set-list?

SHEET MUSIC

You must always bring an original copy of the book or a download sheet with email certificate for each song you perform in the exam. If you choose to write your own song you must provide the examiner with a copy of the sheet music. Your music can be:

* a lead sheet with lyrics, chords and melody line
* a chord chart with lyrics
* a full score using conventional staff notation
* see page 37 for details on presenting a song you have written yourself.

The title of the song and your name should be on the sheet music.

HELP PAGES

WRITING YOUR OWN SONG

You can perform a song that you have written yourself for one of the choices in your exam. For Grade 2, your song should last between one and three-and-a-half minutes, so it is likely to be quite straightforward. It is sometimes difficult to know where to begin, however. Here are some suggestions for starting points:

- **A melody**: many songs are made up around a 'hook' (a short catchy melodic idea, usually only a few notes long).
Try writing a couple of ideas for hooks here:

- **A riff**: A riff is a very short melodic or rhythmic idea which is repeated over and over. It often underpins an entire song. Write a couple of short riffs here:

WRITING YOUR SONG DOWN

Rock and pop music is often written as a **lead sheet** with the lyrics (if there are any), chords and a melody line.

- You can, if you prefer, use a **graph** or **table** to represent your music, as long as it is clear to anyone else (including the examiner) how the song goes.

- **A word or phrase, theme or subject**: certain words and subjects suggest particular styles of music: a song about riding a motorbike might have a driving rhythm, a love song could be more reflective.

There are plenty of other ways of starting: perhaps with a chord sequence or a lyric, for example.

You will also need to consider the **structure** of your song (verse and chorus, 12-bar blues, and so on), the **style** it is in (blues, hard rock, etc.), and what **instruments** it is for (e.g. solo voice or voice/keyboards/drums . . .).

There are many choices to be made – which is why writing a song is such a rewarding thing to do.

PERFORMING IN A BAND

Performing in a band is exciting: it can be a lot of fun and, as with everything, the more you do it, the easier it gets. It is very different from performing on your own. Everyone contributes to the overall sound: the most important skill you need to develop is listening.

For a band to sound good, the players need to be 'together' – that mainly means keeping in time with each other, but also playing at the same volume, and with the same kind of feeling. Your relationship with the other band members is also important. Talk with them about the music you perform, the music you like, and what you'd like the band to achieve short-term and long-term.

Band rehearsals are important – you should not be late, tired or distracted by your mobile phone! Being positive makes a huge difference. Try to create a friendly atmosphere in rehearsals so that everybody feels comfortable trying out new things. Don't worry about making mistakes: that is what rehearsals are for.

'Mean Jumper Blues' on page 14 is arranged for band. You will find parts for keyboards, guitar, bass and drums in the other Trinity Rock & Pop Grade 2 books or available online. Trinity offers exams for groups of musicians at various levels. The songs arranged for bands are ideal to include as part of a set-list for these exams. Have a look at the website for more details.

HINTS AND TIPS

- Your own ability as a musician is important – if you have practised different techniques on your own, then you will have more to offer to the band. It is worth remembering that simple parts can be very effective, it is not always necessary for each instrument to play every note in the chord, or on every beat of the bar.

- Listen to how your part fits with the rest of the band. Each person should contribute something different to the overall sound: having different people sing and play similar parts rarely sounds good.

- Some instruments could stop playing in certain sections. This is a very effective way of increasing the range of dynamics.

SINGING WITH BACKING TRACKS

The CD contains demos and backing tracks of all the songs in the book. The additional songs at www.trinityrock.com/downloads also come with demos and backing tracks.

- In your exam, you should perform with the backing track, or you can create your own (see below).
- The backing tracks begin with a click track, which sets the tempo and helps you start accurately.
- Be careful to balance the volume of the backing track against your voice.
- Listen carefully to the backing track to ensure you are singing in time.

If you are creating your own backing track here are some further tips:

- Make sure the sound quality is of a good standard.
- Think carefully about the instruments/sounds you are putting on the backing track.
- Avoid copying what you are singing on the backing track – it should support not duplicate.
- Do you need to include a click track at the beginning?

COPYRIGHT IN A SONG

If you are a singer or songwriter it is important to know about copyright. When someone writes a song or creates an arrangement they own the copyright (sometimes called 'the rights') to that version. The copyright means that other people cannot copy it, sell it, perform it in a concert, make it available online or record it without the owner's permission or the appropriate licence. When you write a song you automatically own the copyright to it, which means that other people cannot copy your work. But, just as importantly, you cannot copy other people's work, or perform it in public without their permission or the appropriate licence.

Points to remember

- You can create a cover version of a song and play it in an exam or other non-public performance.
- You cannot record your cover version and make your recording available to others (by copying it or uploading it to a website) without the appropriate licence.
- You do own the copyright of your own original song, which means that no one is allowed to copy it.
- You cannot copy someone else's song without their permission or the appropriate licence.

ALSO AVAILABLE

Trinity College London Rock & Pop examinations 2012-2017 are also available for:

Bass Initial
ISBN: 978-0-85736-227-8

Bass Grade 1
ISBN: 978-0-85736-228-5

Bass Grade 2
ISBN: 978-0-85736-229-2

Bass Grade 3
ISBN: 978-0-85736-230-8

Bass Grade 4
ISBN: 978-0-85736-231-5

Bass Grade 5
ISBN: 978-0-85736-232-2

Bass Grade 6
ISBN: 978-0-85736-233-9

Bass Grade 7
ISBN: 978-0-85736-234-6

Bass Grade 8
ISBN: 978-0-85736-235-3

Drums Initial
ISBN: 978-0-85736-245-2

Drums Grade 1
ISBN: 978-0-85736-246-9

Drums Grade 2
ISBN: 978-0-85736-247-6

Drums Grade 3
ISBN: 978-0-85736-248-3

Drums Grade 4
ISBN: 978-0-85736-249-0

Drums Grade 5
ISBN: 978-0-85736-250-6

Drums Grade 6
ISBN: 978-0-85736-251-3

Drums Grade 7
ISBN: 978-0-85736-252-0

Drums Grade 8
ISBN: 978-0-85736-253-7

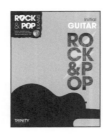

Guitar Initial
ISBN: 978-0-85736-218-6

Guitar Grade 1
ISBN: 978-0-85736-219-3

Guitar Grade 2
ISBN: 978-0-85736-220-9

Guitar Grade 3
ISBN: 978-0-85736-221-6

Guitar Grade 4
ISBN: 978-0-85736-222-3

Guitar Grade 5
ISBN: 978-0-85736-223-0

Guitar Grade 6
ISBN: 978-0-85736-224-7

Guitar Grade 7
ISBN: 978-0-85736-225-4

Guitar Grade 8
ISBN: 978-0-85736-226-1

Keyboards Initial
ISBN: 978-0-85736-236-0

Keyboards Grade 1
ISBN: 978-0-85736-237-7

Keyboards Grade 2
ISBN: 978-0-85736-238-4

Keyboards Grade 3
ISBN: 978-0-85736-239-1

Keyboards Grade 4
ISBN: 978-0-85736-240-7

Keyboards Grade 5
ISBN: 978-0-85736-241-4

Keyboards Grade 6
ISBN: 978-0-85736-242-1

Keyboards Grade 7
ISBN: 978-0-85736-243-8

Keyboards Grade 8
ISBN: 978-0-85736-244-5

Vocals Initial
ISBN: 978-0-85736-254-4

Vocals Grade 1
ISBN: 978-0-85736-255-1

Vocals Grade 2
ISBN: 978-0-85736-256-8

Vocals Grade 3
ISBN: 978-0-85736-257-5

Vocals Grade 4
ISBN: 978-0-85736-258-2

Vocals Grade 5
ISBN: 978-0-85736-259-9

Vocals Grade 6 (female voice)
ISBN: 978-0-85736-263-6

Vocals Grade 6 (male voice)
ISBN: 978-0-85736-260-5

Vocals Grade 7 (female voice)
ISBN: 978-0-85736-264-3

Vocals Grade 7 (male voice)
ISBN: 978-0-85736-261-2

Vocals Grade 8 (female voice)
ISBN: 978-0-85736-265-0

Vocals Grade 8 (male voice)
ISBN: 978-0-85736-262-9